白蛇传

MADAM WHITE SNAKE

雷峰塔下的传奇

蔡志忠/著　Joyce Lim/译

蔡志忠漫画中英文版

现代出版社

Madam White Snake

雷峰塔下的传奇——白蛇传

写成一个善解人意的可爱女性。

蛇也仍然只是个专门吃人的可怕妖怪。从《白娘子永镇雷峰塔》这篇以后，所有的白蛇故事，才都将白蛇性的女妖，却是从这一篇《白娘子永镇雷峰塔》才开始。在六十家小说所收的话本《西湖三塔记》里，白

关于白蛇化身为人，蛊惑男人的故事虽然可以上溯到唐代的传奇小说，但是，真正将白蛇写成一个很有人

本书故事选自《警世通言》第二十八卷。白娘子的故事是流通很广的一个民间故事，几乎家喻户晓。

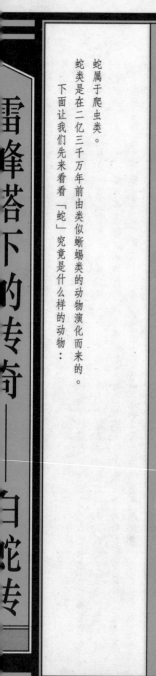

蛇属于爬虫类。

蛇类是在二亿三千万年前由类似蜥蜴类的动物演化而来的。

下面让我们先来看看「蛇」究竟是什么样的动物：

The scenery is beautiful. When will the revelry end? Lulled by the breeze, we are back in Bianzhou.

Clap!

Clap!

Today, I'm going to tell you a story about the legend of the Leifeng Pagoda at West Lake.

Madam White Snake

Storyteller

The protagonist of our story is a white snake with a very attractive figure and was enchantingly pretty.

Storyteller

What a joke! Snakes are so ugly. Who'll be enchanted by them?

There's a part of you that resembles a snake and it's very alluring.

Nonsense! Which part?

Storyteller

Your waist!

...

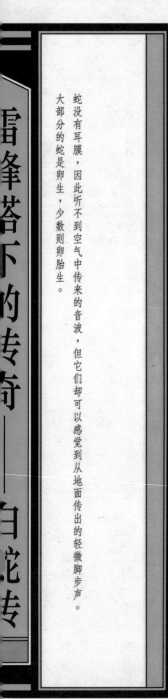

蛇没有耳膜，因此听不到空气中传来的音波，但它们却可以感觉到从地面传出的轻微脚步声。

大部分的蛇是卵生，少数则卵胎生。

Tempted by the serpent, Adam and Eve ate fruits from the tree. As punishment, they were banished from the Garden of Eden.

The serpent is the Devil, Satan incarnate.

Ouch!

What's wrong with being a devil?

Wouldn't the world be a boring place without the Devil's temptations?

I simply love devils!

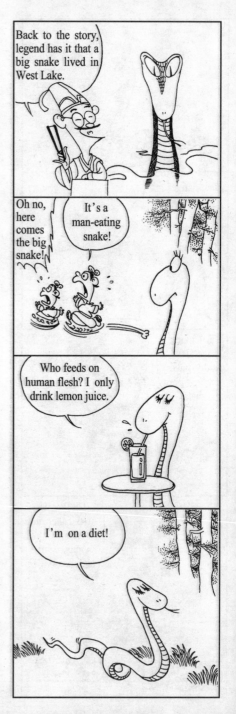

Back to the story, legend has it that a big snake lived in West Lake.

Oh no, here comes the big snake!

It's a man-eating snake!

Who feeds on human flesh? I only drink lemon juice.

I'm on a diet!

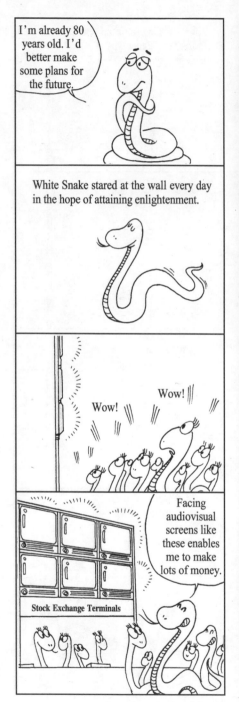

蛇身上的鳞片，是保护它身体的「盔甲」，也是爬行时惟一依靠的工具。

蛇没有胸骨，若将蛇倒提着抖一抖，它的脊椎骨便会脱白，脊髓受到严重损害，蛇就一命呜呼了。

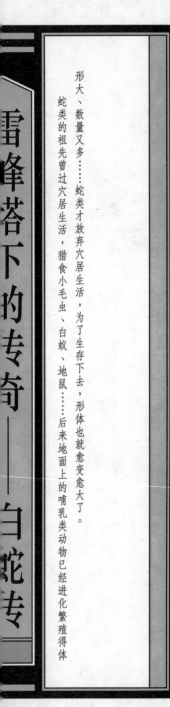

形大、数量又多……蛇类才放弃穴居生活，为了生存下去，形体也就愈变愈大了。

蛇类的祖先曾过穴居生活，猎食小毛虫、白蚁、地鼠……后来地面上的哺乳类动物已经进化繁殖得体

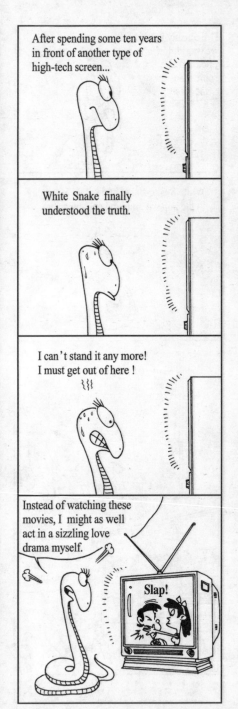

After spending some ten years in front of another type of high-tech screen...

White Snake finally understood the truth.

I can't stand it any more! I must get out of here !

Instead of watching these movies, I might as well act in a sizzling love drama myself.

Slap!

To be the lead actress, I must first turn myself into a woman.

As long as you're willing to spend some money, it can be done.

I've made a pile from the stock market. Money is not a problem.

That's good!

Cosmetic Surgery Hospital

The implants for the breasts, nose and buttocks will cost 2m units of cash. I guarantee you'll become a real woman.

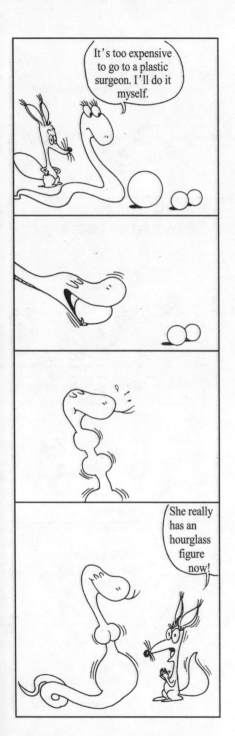

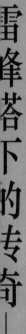

雷峰塔下的传奇——白蛇传

故事。

这些名胜古迹之所以引人幽思，使人流连，是因为在它们的背后，往往有一个悠远的传说，或美丽的

杭州西湖的胜景，自古天下闻名，不只山光秀丽，水色宜人，更多的是名胜古迹，引人幽思。

暖风薰得游人醉，直把杭州作汴州。

山外青山楼外楼，西湖歌舞几时休？

Living in the waters just below the third bridge in West Lake was a thousand-year-old carp.

I like it here. Many tourists visit the lake, so there's no shortage of food.

On Sundays and public holidays, I get to eat more food, and to play the game of death.

The thousand-year-old carp spent all her time swimming in the lake and leading a very carefree life.

I'm a beautiful girl of eighteen who has yet to find a good husband.

Though the thousand-year-old carp was a great beauty, she had a problem.

Oh, why must there be whiskers on my beautiful face?

「涌金门」。

后，便不见了。杭州城的人认为这是神灵显化，便在山腰立了一个寺庙，这就是金山寺。而西门从此便叫西门。眼见全城即将遭殃，忽然水中涌现一头全身金色的牛，不久洪水即退。而那只金牛随水流到北山之金山寺、涌金门的由来，据说就是因为在晋朝咸和年间，有一次山洪爆发，水势汹涌，惊涛骇浪冲入

9

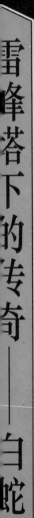

雷峰塔下的传奇——白蛇传

不信的话，让我呼叫它出来。」一呼叫，果然跑出了一只白猿。从此，大家便称这座山峰为飞来峰。

的人都不相信，僧人说：「我记得灵鹫山前的这座峰岭，叫做灵鹫岭，上面有一个山洞，洞里有只白猿。

余，看到这一座突出的山峰，便说：「印度灵鹫山前的一座小峰，忽然不见，原来就是飞到这里。」当时

飞来峰的神话也很神奇。听说以前有一位西域来的僧人，名叫浑寿罗，云游到杭州西湖，观赏山景之

10

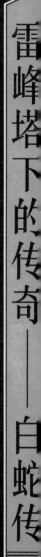

和靖先生筑的。另外又有白公堤、苏公堤。

而湖中有一座山，叫做孤山，旁边有一条路，东接断桥，西接霞岭，叫做孤山路，便是宋朝的隐士林

雷峰塔下的传奇——白蛇传

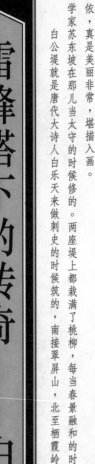

依，真是美丽非常，堪描入画。

学家苏东坡在那儿当太守的时候修的。两座堤上都栽满了桃柳，每当春景融和的时节，桃花飘香，杨柳依

白公堤就是唐代大诗人白乐天来做刺史的时候筑的，南接翠屏山，北至栖霞岭。苏公堤则是北宋大文

As a carp or a snake, we needn't worry about our livelihood. But as human beings now, we have to work for a living.

That's exactly what we're doing now.

What? You call sitting around and chatting work?

Well, now we're appearing in the comic strip, *Madam White Snake*.

Every time we make an appearance, we get 2,000 units of cash!

Lianhe Bao Accounts Section

I'll prepare some food for my mistress.

That's my favourite dish!

Steamed Frogs!

For a change, I'll do the cooking tomorrow.

Do you know what I like?

Of course I do!

Wow! Live earthworms!

各位读者，或许你们会说，正经儿的故事不说，却讲这些古迹传说干什么！这有个缘故，本书要说的

这一篇故事，正和西湖一个古迹的传说有关，所以在正题儿未讲之先，便先引这几个有关名人古迹的传

说，来做个开场。

雷峰塔下的传奇——白蛇传

13

《雷峰塔下的传奇——白蛇传》

故事就发生在南宋绍兴年间的杭州府。

有些悲怨凄怆的故事。

什么有这雷峰塔？各位恐怕就不一定清楚了。原来雷峰塔的建立，关联着一个稀奇古怪、美丽风流，却又我们今天要说的故事，就是西湖雷峰塔的传奇。雷峰塔是杭州的名胜，这是各位都知道的。但是，为

When choosing a partner, it's important that we find someone from a similar background, with a well-matched temperament.

I know of someone who fits the bill! I'll get him here right away!

He's indeed a fine-looking man.

As the saying goes, a couple has to be well-matched!

Since you're Madam Snake and I'm Mister Snake, we're definitely well-matched!

It's said that in Lin'an county in Hangzhou, there lived a Xu family who owned a medical hall.

The Xu family had only one male heir in three generations.

Xu Xian, we're counting on you to carry on the family name.

Father.

"Two is ideal, one is good enough!" You deserve this award.

Oh no, I don't deserve this honour!

Model of Family Planning

Actually, my wife had already given birth to ten girls before we had Xu Xian!

...

话说杭州城中官巷口李家草药铺中，有一位年轻的伙计，名叫许仙，今年二十二岁，尚未成亲。这许

仙上无兄、下无弟，父母就单单生下他和一个姐姐，按排行来说，也算是老大，因此家人便又叫他小乙。

孤孤凄凄的小乙一个人，好不可怜。亏得姐姐、姐夫怜他一个少年人家，无人照管，便将他接过来同住。

小乙的爹原也是开草药铺的，不幸在他十五岁那年，父母相继病亡，当时姐姐又已出嫁，家中便落得

管钱粮。这种军需官在当时又称募事官，所以人家便叫他李募事。

小乙的姐夫姓李名仁，家住城中过军桥黑珠巷内，是邵太尉手下一名小小的军需官，平常也替邵太尉

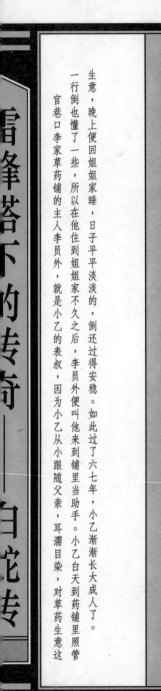

生意，晚上便回姐姐家睡，日子平平淡淡的，倒还过得安稳。如此过了六七年，小乙渐渐长大成人了。

一行倒也懂了一些，所以在他住到姐姐家不久之后，李员外便叫他来到铺里当助手。小乙白天到药铺里照管

官巷口李家草药铺的主人李员外，就是小乙的表叔，因为小乙从小跟随父亲，耳濡目染，对草药生意这

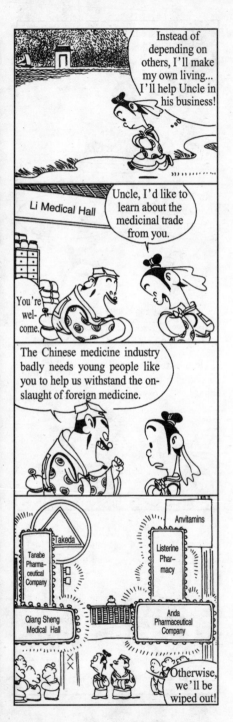

Summer is not a suitable time for selling tonics. Our business is getting from bad to worse.

Don't worry, Uncle.

We need some business acumen here. We should sell something suitable for consumption in summer.

Just add some ingredients to the medicinal herbs and I guarantee we'll have good business.

Try our cooling green jelly tea!

Green jelly tea

Sour plum soup

Bitter gourd tea

Wax gourd tea

One glass, please.

I would like to go to Baoshu Pagoda and pay respects to my ancestors. May I?

You should.

Li Medical Hall

The weather is unpredictable during *Qing Ming**. Take an umbrella with you.

Yes.

This umbrella was made by the Shu family at Lake Qing. It has eighty-four frames and a black bamboo handle. It's worth 5 million units of cash.

That expensive?

* The Tomb-sweeping Festival.

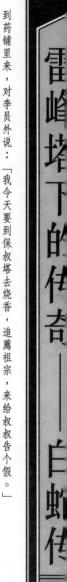

到药铺里来，对李员外说：「我今天要到保叔塔去烧香，追荐祖宗，来给叔叔告个假。」

第二天早起，便先去买了蜡烛、冥钱、纸马、香枝等东西。准备妥当，换了新鞋袜、新衣服，然后才

姐姐说：「爹娘过世多年了，这也是应当的。」

叫我明天到寺里烧香，追荐祖宗。我想明天向表叔告个假，去走一趟。」

就在这一年的清明节前夕，小乙回家之后，吃过了晚饭，对姐姐说：「今天保叔塔的和尚到店里去，

雷峰塔下的传奇——白蛇传

托。」

何是好，只见一个老儿，摇着一只船过来，小乙认得是张阿公，大喜，叫道：「张阿公，载我过湖去，拜

眼见得地下湿了，小乙可惜新鞋袜，便脱了下来，赤脚走出四圣观来寻船，却没见到半只。正不知如

渐大，正是清明时节，少不得天公应时，催花雨下，那阵雨下得绵绵不绝。

谁知这清明天气，惯会捉弄人。忽然云生西北，雾锁东南，下起微微的细雨来了。不一会儿，雨渐下

雷峰塔下的传奇　白蛇传

船刚摇离了岸七八丈远，忽然岸上有人叫道：「公公，拜托一下，我们要搭船过湖。」原来是一个妇人和一个丫环。张阿公将船又摇过岸边，接那妇人同丫环上船。小乙见那妇人头上梳着孝髻，身上穿一件白绢衫儿，上穿一条细麻布裙。丫环头上一双角髻，身上穿着青色衣服，手中捧着一个包儿。

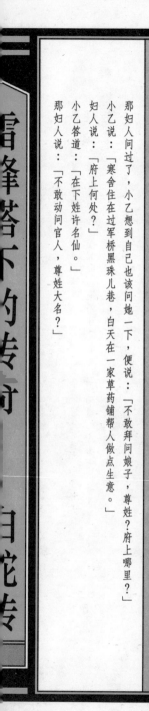

那妇人问过了，小乙想到自己也该问她一下，便说：「不敢拜问娘子，尊姓？府上哪里？」

小乙说：「寒舍住在过军桥黑珠儿巷，白天在一家草药铺帮人做点生意。」

妇人说：「府上何处？」

小乙答道：「在下姓许名仙。」

那妇人说：：「不敢动问官人，尊姓大名？」

沥地下着。

小乙说：「娘子请便，这一点点船钱，不算什么。」算还了船钱，小乙搀那妇人上岸，雨还是浙浙沥沥上祭扫，刚要回去，不巧就遇上了这场雨。如果不是搭了官人的便船，不知该如何是好！

那妇人说：「奴家白氏，亡夫姓张。亡夫年前不幸过世，就葬在雷岭这边。今天清明，带了丫环来坟

小乙说：「这点小事何须挂怀。天色晚了，容改天再来拜望吧！」

那妇人说：「寒舍就在箭桥双茶坊巷口，若不嫌弃，请到寒舍奉茶，一并送还船钱。」

雷峰塔下的传奇——白蛇传

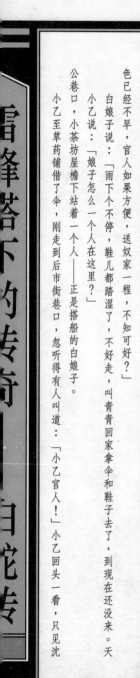

The next day, Xu Xian made a trip to Arrow Bridge to look for Madam White Snake.

Could you tell me if there's a White Mansion in the vicinity?

This is a slum area—of course there's no mansion here. But strangely enough, a very grand house sprang up here overnight.

A house built in just a day?

Such model houses can be put up in no time.

West Lake Buliders Construction Site

Model House

Madam White's residence is indeed grandiose.

You've kept your promise to come.

What a grand house this is!

This is only a facade.

It's just a prop, so you don't need a complete structure.

...

霍峰塔下的传奇——白蛇传

白娘子在里头应道：「请官人进里面奉茶。」

青青说：「官人，请到里面坐。」又向里面悄悄地叫声：「娘子，许官人来了。」

青青说：「官人跟我来。」带着小乙走了一段路，来到一家楼房门前，说：「这里便是。」

正在那儿不知所措，青青正好从东边走来。小乙说：「你家在哪里啊？我来拿伞，找白娘子。问了好久都找不到。」

隔天，小乙离了店，一路便到箭桥双茶坊巷口来，找白娘子。问了半天，并没一个人认得。

下来。」

白娘子说：「这倒不须官人烦恼，奴家身边还有些余财，可以用得。」便叫青青：「你去取一锭白银

小乙说：「实不相瞒，只因在下身边窘迫，不敢从命。」

且一见便蒙错爱，正是你有心我有意。如不嫌弃，就请央一个媒人，共成百年姻眷。想必你我宿世有缘，才有这番巧遇。而

家看你是个老实人，真人面前说不得假话。奴家的丈夫过世经年，不知意下如何？」

小乙坐下。白娘子给他倒了一杯酒，劝他喝了，又倒一杯，带着满面春风，娇滴滴地说：「官人，奴

Don't worry about money.

I come from a very poor family, and cannot afford to take a wife.

You may have these two silver ingots.

Xiaoqing, thank you for thinking so highly of me. I'll return you the money some other day.

I'll charge you 10% interest for the loan and of course, you're the mortgage.

10% Int

Xiaoqing, I'll go home and get a matchmaker to ask for Madam White's hand.

Just a minute! We should put this down in black and white.

Both parties will need to sign an engagement certificate.

Can I leave now?

Hold on!

...

You'll have to sign an IOU.

26

One roast goose, please!

Xu Xian decided to ask his sister to be the matchmaker, so he bought some fish and meat from the street market.

Two bottles of the best liquor, please.

Okay!

XO, our best brand of liquor. Each bottle costs 8,671 units of cash.

This is indeed a strong brew. The mere mention of its price is enough to knock him out.

My dear sister and brother-in-law, join me in the feast.

You hardly ever touch liquor. Why the sudden splurge?

I have some good news to announce, but let's have a drink first.

Cheers!

Cheers!

Brother, you still haven't told us the good news.

Gosh, I can't remember what it is!

喝了几杯，姐夫憋不住闷葫芦，便说：「小乙，无缘无故地花钱，有什么事吗？」

天不知为了什么事？」

那天刚好姐夫也早些回来，听说小乙摆了酒席请他，好生奇怪，想道：「小乙平常俭省得不得了，今

酒。

烧鹅、鲜鱼、精肉、嫩鸡、果品等等，提回家来了。又买了一樽酒，安排了一桌酒席，来请姐夫和姐姐吃

隔天，小乙把伞送还了李员外，仍照常到铺里照管生意。到得下午，又给李员外告个假，到市场买了

27

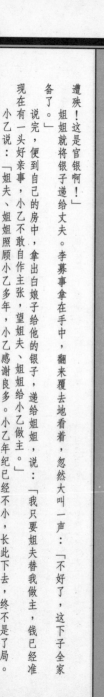

遭殃！这是官银啊！」

姐姐就将银子递给丈夫。李募事拿在手中，翻来覆去地看着，忽然大叫一声：「不好了，这下子全家备了。」

说完，便到自己的房中，拿出白娘子给他的银子，递给姐姐，说：「我只要姐夫替我做主，钱已经准现在有一头好亲事，小乙不敢自作主张，望姐夫、姐姐给小乙做主。」

小乙说：「姐夫、姐姐照顾小乙多年，小乙感谢良多。小乙年纪已经不小，长此下去，终不是了局。」

Xu Xian recounted how he had met the two women after a visit to the cemetery.

I hope to marry the young lady and her maid. May I have your consent?

You have my full support. I'll share the responsibility with you.

I'll take care of one lady and you, the other.

Madam White agreed to marry me yesterday and gave me these two silver ingots. Sis, could you ask for her hand on my behalf?

She's indeed from a rich family!

The official stamp shows that these are silver ingots stolen from the treasury.

Madam White is no thief! The ingots must have run away on their own, and were picked up by her.

Ingots don't have legs. How could they have run away from the treasury?

Who says they can't run away? I actually had two silver ingots, one of which made its way to the goose-seller's purse.

府尹见了，也不问话，只喝声：「打！」

何立带了一班衙役，火速赶到官巷口李家药铺，见了小乙，不由分说，绑了就走。即刻解到府里来。

前去抓人。

李募事当时拿了银子到府里出首，府尹听说有了贼赃，整个晚上再也睡不着。第二天上堂差捕头何立

他的妻子听得目瞪口呆，出声不得。

着，哪里像是有人住的样子？众人都呆住了，小乙更是惊得张了口合不得。

一行人扰扰嚷嚷地赶到秀王府对面楼房一看，门前一堆垃圾，也不知堆了多久了…大门一条竹竿横夹

府尹即叫何立带领从人，押着小乙去捉白娘子。

小乙说："住在箭桥边，双茶坊巷口，秀王王府对面的楼房。"

府尹说："白娘子现在何处？"

小乙便将遇见白娘子的事情，前前后后说了一遍。

Make a thorough search!

The silver ingots from the treasury are still intact here!

Sir, we can't find the two women except for the silver ingots on the bed.

How am I going to close the case?

Bring the silver ingots back to be prosecuted. They shall be charged with absence without leave.

We're innocent!

Wah!

Xu Xian received a light sentence and was banished to Zhenjiang.

My poor brother-fancy being banished to such a faraway place at such a young age!

It was my idea!

Why did you do such a thing?

Troublesome relatives should be kept at arm's length!

雷峰塔下的传奇——白蛇传

主人说："你等一等，我去叫他出来。"

丫环说："我找杭州府来的许仙官人。"

王主人说："这里就是，不知你找谁？"

主人家吗？"

人往，忽然一乘轿子，旁边一个丫环跟着，来到门前停了下来。那丫环向前问道："借问一下，这里是王主人家吗？"

小乙被发配到苏州，后来住在王主人家，时当九月下旬，有一天，王主人正在门口闲站，看街上人来

便走到里面叫着："小乙哥，有人找你。"

31

白娘子解释过后，王主人说：「既然当初曾许嫁小乙哥，那就更不用回去了，你就留下来吧！」

白娘子道：「官人，不要怪我，这次来，是特地来给你分辩这件事的。让我们到主人家里面说。」说着，便叫青青取了包裹下轿。

不差死人么！」

道：「死冤家！你盗了官库银子，劳累我吃了多少苦！有冤无处伸！如今落得如此下场，你还来干什么？

小乙听了，忽走出来，到门前看时，那丫环正是青青，轿里坐的正是白娘子，不禁气往上冲，连声叫

If you were innocent, why would you give me silver ingots stolen from the treasury?

Master Xu, this is a misunderstanding.

My late husband left me the silver ingots. I have no idea they were stolen property.

Did you know I almost had to go to jail because of those ingots?

It's a pity you didn't go to jail.

Otherwise, you'd have a good excuse to stand for election as a people's representative!

The next day, Xiaoqing set off to look for a place to stay.

I've booked all the 300 rooms in this hotel!

There are only three of us. Why did you do so?

We can sub-let the other rooms and make a profit from it!

But we'll have to convert the hotel into a hospital first. Then we'll make money.

主人说：「今天是二月半，大家都去承天寺看卧佛。你也好去逛逛。」

子？怎地如此热闹？」

个月过去。时当春景融合，花开似锦，街坊上车马往来，热闹非常。小乙问主人家道：「今天是什么日

番情味，新婚之乐，自不必说。以后生活，都是白娘子拿钱出来用度。日往月来，自从两人成亲，又是几

光阴一瞬，早到吉日良时。白娘子取出银两，央王主人备办喜筵，二人拜堂成亲，异地完婚，别是一

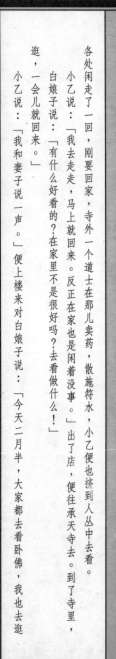

各处闲走了一回，刚要回家，寺外一个道士在那儿卖药，散施符水，小乙便也挤到人丛中去看。

小乙说：「我去走走，马上就回来。反正在家里也是闲着没事。」出了店，便往承天寺去。到了寺里，

白娘子说：「有什么好看的？在家里不是很好吗？去看做什么！」

小乙说：「我和妻子说一声。」便上楼来对白娘子说：「今天二月半，大家都去看卧佛，我也去逛

逛，一会儿就回来。」

Business is so poor. We hardly have any patients.

Ever since we set up the hospital, I've been hoping that everybody will fall ill. Have I really become that wicked?

Well, if you were a coffin-maker, you'd naturally hope that more people would die too!

Since we don't have any patients, we should change our management style, and treat those who are healthy instead.

Perfectly healthy people go to hospitals too?

Honest to Goodness Cosmetic Surgery Hospital

There really are such people!

You need to have the bridge of your nose raised, your lips made thin, and the freckles on your face removed.

Yes!

Xiaoqing, where's my lunch?

Ha! Ha! I've been so busy that I forgot to fix lunch!

I have no time to go to the market, so we'll have to make do with whatever is available.

Capsules, vitamin pills and glucose sweets— they provide you with all the nutrition you need!

...

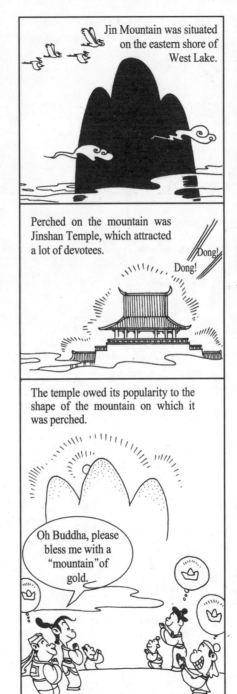

白娘子说：「我以前未嫁时，也学了些道术，明天便同你去看，是怎么样的一个道士。」

小乙说：「这不干我事，是承天寺前一个云游道士教我的，他说你是妖怪。」

说罢，也不等小乙回答，一把夺过符来，就在灯前烧化了，却全无动静。白娘子说：「我是妖怪吗？」

随便就相信别人的话？半夜三更，你烧符干什么？是不是要来镇压我？你就烧吧！」

化，忽听得白娘子叹了一口气：「小乙哥，做夫妻那么久，一向我待你也不薄，为什么你老是疑神疑鬼，

等到晚上三更，小乙料想白娘子和青青都睡熟了，便起身将一道符放在头发内，正要将另一道符烧

Jinshan Temple was headed by the Abbot Fa Hai.

Be gone, you accursed spirit!

Fa Hai was well respected among the devotees, and was famous for subduing evil spirits.

He was a very demanding person who could not tolerate any imperfections.

It's half an inch longer than it should be...

The Abbot's room should measure one *zhang* by one *zhang*, not an inch more nor an inch less!

Yes, Teacher.

Teacher, Jinshan Temple is so run-down, it badly needs some renovations.

The more run-down the temple is, the better.

If we build a suspension bridge, we'll attract even bigger crowds.

We're on the way to Jinshan Temple.

Let's make a trip to Jinshan Temple.

* One *zhang* = 3.33 metres.

那道士说：「我行的是五雷天心正法，凡有妖怪，吃了我的符，即刻便现出原形。」

说人家是妖怪！你画符来我看看！」

白娘子对小乙说：「我先试他道行看看。」走到道士面前，大喝一声：「你好无礼！出家人怎么随便士仍在那儿散施符水，旁边围了一群人。

第二天清早，夫妻两人梳洗罢，白娘子穿了素净衣服，吩咐青青在家，便一同往承天寺前来。那个道

白娘子说：「众人在此，你且画符来让我吃吃看！」

白娘子说：「一个好好的妇人家，怎么说是妖怪呢？」大家你一言我一语地骂那道士。道士被骂得目瞪口呆，说不出话来，惶恐满面。那道士画一道符，递给白娘子。白娘子接过来，一口吞了下去。众人看看并没些影响，便起哄说：

白娘子说：「他欺骗无知便罢，还血口喷人，实在可恶！我从小也学了些戏法，就和你玩玩试试。」

Under the orders of his teacher, Fa Ming made his way to Suzhou in search of Xu Xian...

Registration Counter

Amitabha, I wish to see Mr Xu regarding a very urgent matter.

What's your name? How old are you? Where do you live?

My name is Fa Ming. I'm twenty-one and I live at Jinshan Temple.

Registration Counter

This is your number, and the fee for the Emergency Department is three taels of silver.

My name is Fa Ming. My teacher sent me here to get you out of trouble.

Sir, what can I do for you?

Sir, you've been bewitched by an evil spirit. Your wife, Madam White is actually a thousand-year-old snake spirit, and your maid Xiaoqing, a fish spirit.

Really?

You wicked monk! How dare you tell tales, and accuse me of being a fish spirit!

Witch, you'd better reveal your true self!

Very well, I'll let you have a look at my true self! How dare you call me a fish spirit?

My God! What a superb figure she's got! She's really a beautiful fish spirit!

霍峰塔下的传奇——白蛇传

少生了两条腿，飞也似的走了。众人看完好戏，也就散了，他夫妻两人回家，仍如以往度日，不在话下。

白娘子说：「如果不是看众位面上，我便吊他一年半载！」喷口气，那道士立刻恢复原状，只恨爹娘看了，都吃一惊，小乙却呆住了。

只见白娘子口中喃喃的，不知念些什么，那道士忽然好像被人擒住一般，缩作一团，悬空而起。众人

39

雷峰塔下的传奇——白蛇传

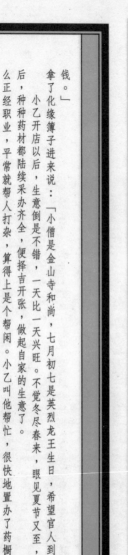

不久之后，小乙拿了银子，约了隔壁的蒋和做伴，到镇江渡口码头上去租了一间房子。这蒋和也没什么正经职业，平常就帮人打杂，算得上是个帮闲。小乙叫他帮忙，很快地置办了药橱、药柜，到十月前后，种种药材都陆续采办齐全，便择吉开张，做起自家的生意了。小乙开店以后，生意倒是不错，一天比一天兴旺。不觉冬尽春来，眼见夏节又至，有一天，一个和尚拿了化缘簿子进来说：「小僧是金山寺和尚，七月初七是英烈龙王生日，希望官人到寺烧香，布施些香钱。」

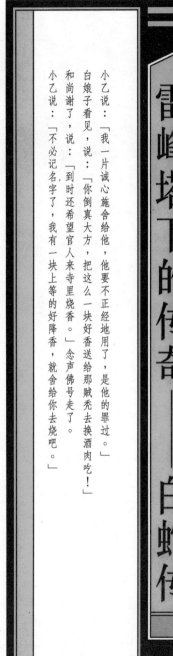

小乙说：「我一片诚心施舍给他，他要不正经地用了，是他的罪过。」

白娘子看见，说：「你倒真大方，把这么一块好香送给那贼秃去换酒肉吃！」

和尚谢了，说：「到时还希望官人来寺里烧香。」念声佛号走了。

小乙说：「不必记名字了，我有一块上等的好降香，就舍给你去烧吧。」

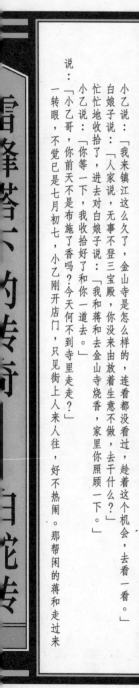

说：「小乙哥，你前天不是布施了香吗？今天何不到寺里走走？」

一转眼，不觉已是七月初七，小乙刚开店门，只见街上人来人往，好不热闹。那帮闲的蒋和走过来

小乙说：「你等一下，我收拾好了和你一道去。」

小乙说：「我和蒋和去金山寺烧香，家里你照顾一下。」

忙忙地收拾了，进去对白娘子说：「我和蒋和去金山寺烧香，家里你照顾一下。」

白娘子说：「人家说，无事不登三宝殿，你没来由放着生意不做，去干什么？」

小乙说：「我来镇江这么久了，金山寺是怎么样的，连看都没看过，趁着这个机会，去看一看。」

Very well, I'll just take a sip.

This is such a happy occasion. Can't you make an exception and drink a little? If you don't, I'm going to be very angry.

That's more like it! Hee Hee...

She really looks different now.

Hic!

I might as well drink to my fill!

Cheers!

She's revealed her true colours!

I've had too much of a drink. I'd better stop before I make a fool of myself.

I'll help you to the bed and you can get some rest.

Dearie, have a good rest.

Strange, she hasn't turned into a snake as I've thought she would.

Still, I've seen her for what she really is.

42

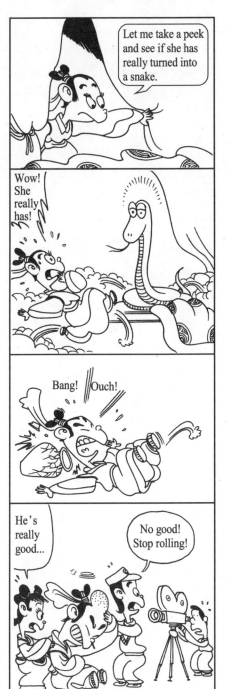

见小乙走过，便叫侍者：「快叫那年轻人进来！」却说方丈里面当中座上坐着一个和尚，方面大耳，一派壮严，看那样子，倒像是个有道行的高僧。一拉着小乙进去看了一会儿，便又出来，却也没什么事。蒋和说：「进去瞧瞧，不碍事的，她在家里，怎么会知道你进去了没有？回家不说就是了。」说着，子叫我不要到里面去。」立住了脚，只在外面张望。到了龙王堂烧了香，寺里各处走了一遍，随着众人信步走到住持所住的方丈门前，猛然猛省道：「娘

44

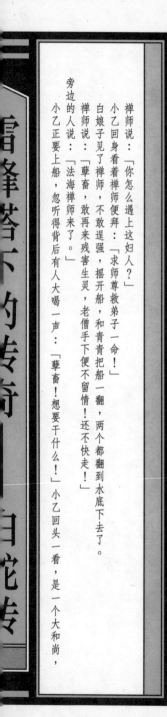

1 *jin* ＝ 0.5kg

精。到了晚上，独自一个人不敢睡，便叫蒋和相伴过夜。可是心里烦闷，哪里睡得着，整夜地辗转反侧。

小乙拜谢了禅师，和蒋和下了渡船回家。回到家时，白娘子和青青都不见了，小乙更相信她们就是妖本是妖精变妇人，西湖岸上卖娇声。汝因不识遭他计，有难湖南见老僧。

西湖南岸净慈寺来找我。」有诗四句：

小乙将事情前后说了一遍。禅师说：「这妇人正是妖怪，现在你就回杭州去。如果再来缠你，你便到

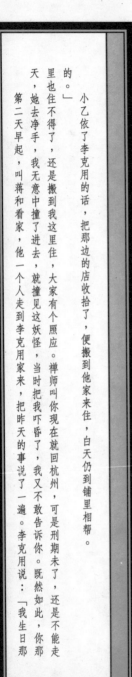

小乙依了李克用的话，把那边的店收拾了，便搬到他家来住，白天仍到铺里相帮。

"里也住不得了，还是搬到我这里住，大家有个照应。禅师叫你现在就回杭州，可是刑期未了，还是不能走的。"

天，她去净手，我无意中撞了进去，就撞见这妖怪，当时把我吓昏了，我又不敢告诉你，你那

第二天早起，叫蒋和看家，他一个人走到李克用家来，把昨天的事说了一遍。李克用说："我生日那

么你在镇江娶了老婆，连写封信来通知一下都没有，难道我们是外人吗？真是无情无义！」

无色，好生奇怪，只见姐夫绷着脸说：「你这个人也太欺负人了，我们一向怎么待你，谅你心里明白！怎

一路饥餐渴饮，夜住晓行，不到几天便已到家。见了姐姐、姐夫，拜了几拜。却见姐姐、姐夫脸上并

赦，欢喜不胜，拜谢了李克用、李妈妈一家，以及东邻西舍，央蒋和买了些土产，便兴冲冲地作别回乡。

两个月后，正值高宗策立孝宗为太子，大赦天下，除了人命大事，其余小事，尽行赦放回家。小乙过

49

老婆呀！」

小乙听了这没来由的话，如坠五里雾中。忽然想到白娘子，心中一阵忐忑，硬着嘴皮说：「我没有娶

李慕事说：「亏你说得出口！你的妻子和丫头现在就在家里，难道会假！你的妻子说你七月初七那天

到金山寺烧香，却一去不回，害她找了好久，找不到人。后来听说你遇赦回乡，她才赶了来，已经等你两

天了。」说着，便叫人请出小乙的妻子和丫头。

Somehow, Xu Xian made his way to Jinshan Temple where he burnt some incense.

Sir, our abbot wishes to speak to you.

Oh!

Reverend Fa Hai, I'm pleased to meet you.

No, thanks. I'd rather stand.

Sir, please take a seat.

Have you forgotten how that woman revealed her real self after she got drunk?

It's strange, but I don't seem to recall...

But I've kept the proof.

She must have used her magic powers to make you forget it.

Really!

Take a look at this report in Lianhe Bao on Aug 29.

儿，看着白娘子笑吟吟的，不由得向前一步，跪在地下，说：「不知娘子是何方神圣？乞饶小人一命！」

当晚，李募事便叫小乙和白娘子同住一房。小乙心中只是害怕，站在房门口，不敢进去，僵持了一会他一场。

头却似乎结住了，一句话也说不出来。李募事看此情形，更认为他是心虚，说不得话，着着实实地埋怨了小乙顿时目瞪口呆，两脚发软——果然是白娘子和青青。心中无限惶恐，又无限委屈，欲待要说，舌

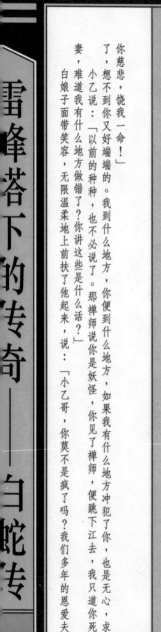

雷峰塔下的传奇——白蛇传

你慈悲，饶我一命！」

了，想不到你又好端端的。我到什么地方，你便到什么地方，如果我有什么地方冲犯了你，也是无心，求

小乙说：「以前的种种，也不必说了。那禅师说你是妖怪，你见了禅师，便跳下江去，我只道你死

妻，难道我有什么地方做错了？你讲这些是什么话？」

白娘子面带笑容，无限温柔地上前扶了他起来，说：「小乙哥，你莫不是疯了吗？我们多年的恩爱夫

52

自己，又有什么好处？可是，大江中风浪涛涛的那一幕，法海禅师一再交待的那些话……难道是我小乙前生罪孽，今生冤孽……

说得小乙半晌无言可答，怔在当地。白娘子的话句句是实，自己孑然一身，她即使是妖是怪，跟定了自己，又有什么好处？可是，大江中风浪涛涛的那一幕，法海禅师一再交待的那些话……难道是我小乙前

疑我！我如果真的另有他图，又何必如此苦苦地跟着你？

夫妻，有什么亏待你之处？一切的一切，还不都是为了你好！谁知你一再相信别人的闲言闲语，一再地怀

白娘子听了，登时变脸，说：「小乙，这样说来，你是信了那妖僧的话了？你也不想想，我和你做了

命，让你后悔不及。我不知道我对你好，是犯了什么罪过，要人家屡次地来破坏！」

愿意听我的话，欢欢喜喜，大家没事。如果你要动歪念头，我叫你满城波涛，人人手攀着洪浪，皆死于非白娘子忍不住气，圆睁怪眼说：「是妖也好，不是妖也好，反正大家扯开了。我老实对你说，如果你小乙还是发怒。对青青的话好像全无知觉。

深情重，听我说，不必再有什么疑虑，一切便都没事了。」

青青看着两人僵持不下，走上前来说：「官人，娘子对你是一片痴情，一番真心，你们夫妻也一向恩

You devils! Instead of meditating in the hills, you've come to wreak havoc in the mortal world! I'm going to subdue you with some chants.

What do you take us for? Some small-time evil spirits? You can chant all you want, but it will have no effect on us!

That's an old-fashioned trick!

I'll use the latest technology, the CD, against you.

Amitabha!

Amitabha!

Amitabha!

I can't stand it any more!

Deity Li, and you warriors up there, please come to my aid!

Don't you try anything funny!

Dong!

Dong!

Dong!

Dong!

Is there no one in the world who's willing to help a damsel in distress?

Our organization's mission is to champion women's rights and to fight against male chauvinist pigs!

House Wife League

Women's Coalition

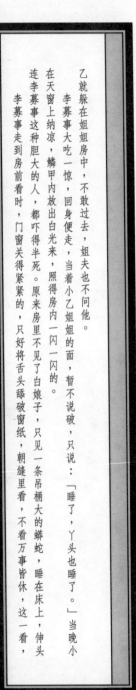

李募事走到房前看时，门窗关得紧紧的，只好将舌头舔破窗纸，朝缝里看，不看万事皆休，这一看，连李募事这种胆大的人，都吓得半死。原来房里不见了白娘子，只见一条吊桶大的蟒蛇，睡在床上，伸头在天窗上纳凉，鳞甲内放出白光来，照得房内一闪一闪的。李募事大吃一惊，回身便走，当着小乙姐姐的面，暂不说破，只说：「睡了，丫头也睡了。」当晚小乙就躲在姐姐房中，不敢过去，姐夫也不问他。

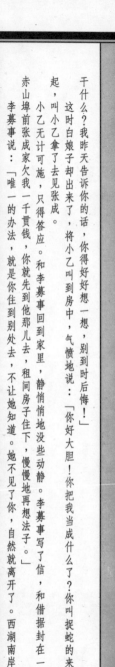

干什么？我昨天告诉你的话，你得好好想一想，别到时后悔！

这时白娘子却出来了，将小乙叫到房中，气愤地说：「你好大胆！你把我当成什么了？你叫捉蛇的来起，叫小乙无计可施，只得答应。和李募事回到家里，静悄悄地没些动静。李募事写了信，和借据封在一小乙拿了去见张成。

赤山埠前张成家欠我一千贯钱，你就先到他那儿去，租间房子住下，慢慢地再想法子。」

李募事说：「唯一的办法，就是你住到别处去，不让她知道。她不见了你，自然就离开了。西湖南岸

寺找我。」

写「净慈寺」三字。小乙登时心中一亮，想起了法海禅师吩咐的话：「如果那妖怪再来缠你，你就来净慈寺找我。」小乙登时心中一亮，想起了法海禅师吩咐的话：「如果那妖怪再来缠你，你就来净慈寺找我。」

走遍了赤山埠路，却哪里找得到！正气闷不已，来到一个地方，想坐下休息，抬头一看，是一座寺庙，上成。见了张成，正要去袖中拿借据，却不见了！这一惊非同小可，心中叫苦，慌忙转身来找。一路上来回小乙听了，不敢作声。袖里藏了书信借据，踱出房来。走到门外，三步作二步地便往赤山埠来找张

59

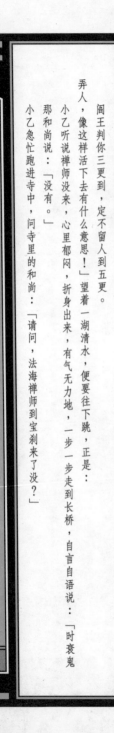

阎王判你三更活到，定不留人到五更。

弄人，像这样活下去有什么意思！」望着一湖清水，便要往下跳，正是：

小乙听说禅师没来，心里郁闷，折身出来，有气无力地，一步一步走到长桥，自言自语说：「时衰鬼

那和尚说：「没有。」

小乙急忙跑进寺中，问寺里的和尚：「请问，法海禅师到宝刹来了没？」

You believed in slanders and cast aside our love. How dare you come back!

I heard that you would be giving birth soon! I can't wait to carry my son, so I rushed home.

The child is not even born yet. How are you going to carry him?

All I have to do is carry the mother as well!

...

My wife is going to give birth today. I'll be a father soon— I'm really excited...

The baby is born!

Wah! Wah!

Strange, how did the baby turn out to be a rag doll?

How did this come about?

The law does not permit infants to act in movies, so we have to make do with a rag doll.

...

60

After giving birth to a son, Madam White became a contented mother. As for Xu Xian, he became a loving husband and doting father.

And the family lived happily ever after...

If the story were to end here, wouldn't I be redundant?

Please don't go! We'll need you in the last act when Fa Hai subdues the demon!

She's looking into the mirror now. Here's the chance I've been waiting for.

Wah!

Dearie, please forgive me!

Ah!

My dear, what are you doing?

It's a new hairdo for you after your confinement!

Not bad at all! It's fashionable and makes me look younger.

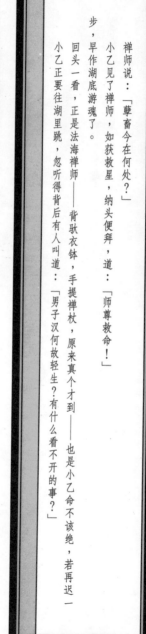

禅师说：「孽畜今在何处？」

小乙见了禅师，如获救星，纳头便拜，道：「师尊救命！」

步，早作湖底游魂了。

回头一看，正是法海禅师——背驮衣钵，手提禅杖，原来真个才到——也是小乙命不该绝，若再迟一

小乙正要往湖里跳，忽听得背后有人叫道：「男子汉何故轻生？有什么看不开的事？」

雷峰塔下的传奇——白蛇传

61

将钵盂藏在袖中，拜谢了禅师，先自回家。

西不要让那孽畜看见，等她不注意，悄悄地往她头上一罩，紧紧地按住，不要害怕，我随后就来。」小乙

小乙将最近的事向禅师说了。禅师听了，从袖中拿出一个钵盂，递给小乙说：「你现在回去，这个东

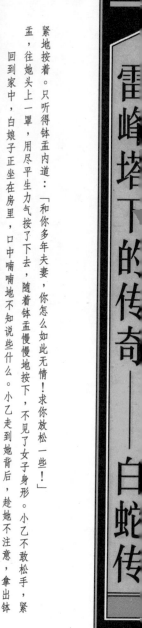

雷峰塔下的传奇——白蛇传

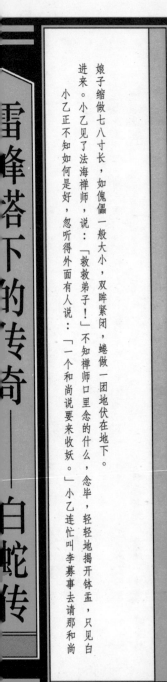

娘子缩做七八寸长，如傀儡一般大小，双眸紧闭，蜷做一团地伏在地下。小乙见了法海禅师，说：「救救弟子！」不知禅师口里念的什么，念毕，轻轻地揭开钵盂，只见白进来。小乙正不知如何是好，忽听得外面有人说：「一个和尚说要来收妖。」小乙连忙叫李募事去请那和尚

Fa Hai proceeded to imprison Madam White Snake in Leifeng Pagoda!

Now that you are trapped inside the pagoda, you won't be able to wreak havoc in the human world.

Says who?

I can have my own version of 'The Lady in the Pagoda'*.

* A Taiwanese movie of the 1960s.

I deserve to be punished for my wrong-doing, but how long will I be imprisoned here?

You'll be released only when the waters in the West Lake dry up, and Leifeng Pagoda collapses!

This is so unfair!

Our right to go on parole!

You can't shut me here indefinitely! Even prisoners sentenced to life imprisonment go on parole!

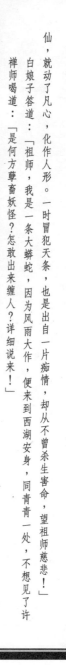

仙，就动了凡心，化作人形。一时冒犯天条，也是出自一片痴情，却从不曾杀生害命，望祖师慈悲！」

白娘子答道：「祖师，我是一条大蟒蛇，因为风雨大作，便来到西湖安身，同青青一处，不想见了许

禅师喝道：「是何方孽畜妖怪？怎敢出来缠人？详细说来！」

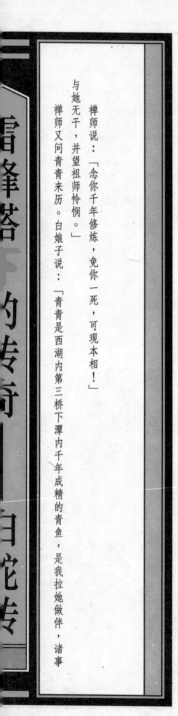

禅师说：「念你千年修炼，免你一死，可现本相！」

与她无干，并望祖师怜悯。」

禅师又问青青来历。白娘子说：「青青是西湖内第三桥下潭内千年成精的青鱼，是我拉她做伴，诸事

A monk leads a more carefree life since he doesn't have to worry about things in the mortal world.

One must be pious as a monk. This is what you need to do every day.

Yes.

The virtue of wisdom is the principal means of attaining Nirvana. There is an emptiness in all things. The immaterial is the material. Nothing is added and nothing is taken away. When there is no desire, there is no pain, no gain or loss.

It's not easy to be a monk after all...

Teacher, though you did a good deed by subduing Madam White Snake, you've got Xiaoqing as your enemy.

There's no gain, no loss, no life, no death.

Number of enemies

正正下

Though I've got myself one more enemy in the form of Xiaoqing...

Number of disciples

正正下

I've got myself another disciple, Xu Xian, so I've neither gained nor lost!

白娘子不肯，抬头呆呆地望着小乙。禅师勃然大怒，口中念念有词，大喝道：「护法尊神何在！快与我把青鱼怪擒来，并令白蛇现形，听吾发落！」禅师话刚说完，庭前忽起一阵狂风，风过处，豁剌剌一声响，半空中坠下一条青鱼，有一丈多长，在地上拨剌剌地跳了几跳，缩作尺多长的一条小青鱼。看那白娘子时，也现了原形——变了一条三尺长白蛇——依然昂着头瞧着小乙。

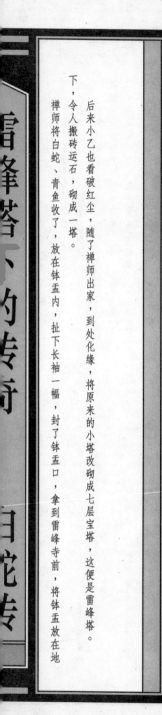

后来小乙也看破红尘，随了禅师出家，到处化缘，将原来的小塔改砌成七层宝塔，这便是雷峰塔。

下，令人搬砖运石，砌成一塔。

禅师将白蛇、青鱼收了，放在钵盂内，扯下长袖一幅，封了钵盂口，拿到雷峰寺前，将钵盂放在地

When Mengjiao was nineteen, he sat for the imperial examinations.

As expected, he passed with flying colours and became a scholar.

Mengjiao's essay is very well-written. It narrates a very touching story. It's excellent in both content and language.

That's because the topic happens to be my pet subject.

Essay topic: My Mother

Mum!

The top scholar is thinking about his mother again! Poor thing!

Mum!

Every small thing reminds him of his mother. How touching!

Mum!

Mum!

But this has gone a bit far!

从此千年万载，白蛇和青鱼永不能出世，除非雷峰塔倒，

雷峰塔倒，白蛇出世。

西湖水干，江湖不起，

禅师见宝塔峰砌成，留偈四句：

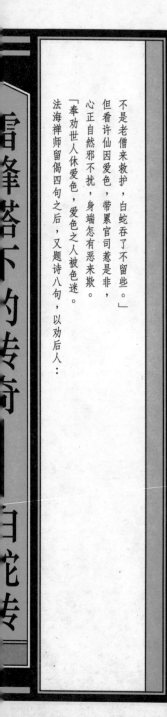

雷峰塔下勺专奇 白蛇专

法海禅师留偈四句之后，又题诗八句，以劝后人：

「奉劝世人休爱色，爱色之人被色迷。

心正自然邪不扰，身端怎有恶来欺。

但看许仙因爱色，带累官司惹是非，

不是老僧来救护，白蛇吞了不留些。」

Xu Mengjiao, you've come at the right time. We're going to demolish Lefeng Pagoda today, so we can release your mother.

Sir, things are different once you're an official. All it took was a little persuasion on your part.

That's true!

This has nothing to do with your persuasive powers.

We need to make way for a new golf course.

To break the curse, all you need to do is count backwards from ten to zero.

It's that simple?

The Curse
1,2,3,4,5,6,
7,8,9,10!

10, 9, 8, 7, 6, 5, 4, 3, 2, 1...

Zero!

众僧将许仙遗体烧化，造了一座骨塔，千年不朽。

法海禅师吟罢，大家都各自散去。只有许仙情愿出家，礼拜禅师为师，在雷峰塔剃度为僧，修行数年，直至坐化而去。

71

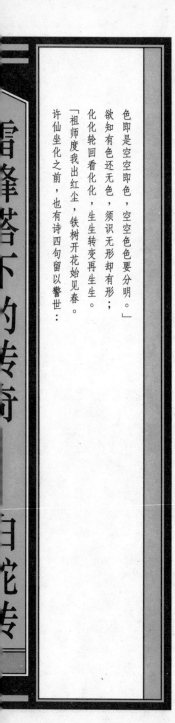

如果以宋人话本的分类来说，应属灵怪类的小说。

词，都是由这一篇衍化而来。

后来《西湖佳话》的《雷峰怪迹》一篇，和清人的《雷峰塔传奇》以及种种白蛇小说，和义妖传弹的意义和价值，是一篇拟话本。

《警世通言》所收的《白娘子永镇雷峰塔》，其来源为《出唐人白蛇记》，这篇白蛇故事，有着其特殊

图字:01－2006－1449

图书在版编目(CIP)数据

白蛇传:雷峰塔下的传奇 = Madam White Snake ／ 蔡志忠绘.
－北京:现代出版社,2006.6
ISBN 7-80188-769-7

Ⅰ.白… Ⅱ.蔡… Ⅲ.漫画-作品集-中国-现代 Ⅳ.J228.2

中国版本图书馆 CIP 数据核字(2006)第 051653 号

Madam White Snake
白蛇传

作者/〔台湾〕蔡志忠
译者/ Joyce Lim
总策划/ 吴江江
责任编辑/ 张璐
封面设计/ 刘刚
出版发行/ 现代出版社(北京安外安华里 504 号　邮编:100011)
印刷/ 世界知识印刷厂
开本/ 880×1230　1/24　　印张/ 3.25
版次/ 2006 年 6 月第 1 版
　　　2006 年 6 月第 1 次印刷
印数/ 1～8000 册
书号/ ISBN　7-80188-769-7
定价/ 8.00 元